Ruby

Scott

Zack

Milly's friends ring the bell. Milly's mum opens the door.

Alesha: Hi, Mrs Green.

Mum: Hi, you lot. Have you come round for Milly?

Scott: Yes. Can she play with us?

Missing Milly

A play by Julia Donaldson

Illustrated by Elina Ellis

Characters

Mum

(Milly's mum)

Alesha

Mum: Of course – come in. I'll just get her. Milly! MILLY! Where are you?

Ruby: I expect she's in her room.

Mum: Let's go up and have a look.

They all go into Milly's bedroom.

Zack: No, she's not here.

Mum: The sheet from her bed is missing too. How odd.

Fred: Maybe Milly's in your bedroom, Mrs Green.

Mum: Why don't we go and see?

They all go into Mrs Green's bedroom.

Alesha: No, she's not here.

Mum: What's happened to my sunglasses? They were here just now.

Scott: Perhaps Milly's in the dining room.

Ruby: Yes, let's go and look there.

They all go into the dining room.

Zack: No, she's not here.

Fred: Where can she be?

Mum: Where have all the apples gone?

Alesha: Do you think she's in the sitting room?

Scott: Yes, I bet she is. Let's have a look.

They all go into the sitting room.

Ruby: No, she's not in here.

Mum: Where are the cushions from the sofa?

They all go out of the room.

Zack: Where do you keep your coats, Mrs Green?

Mum: On the pegs by the back door.

Fred: I bet Milly's there.

Alesha: Yes, perhaps she's hiding behind the coats!

They all go and look.

Scott: No, she's not here.

Mum: Her sun hat is missing too.

Ruby: Look, the back door is open!

Zack: Maybe Milly's playing in the garden.

Fred: Let's go out and have a look.

They all go into the garden.

Alesha: Milly! Milly!

Scott: There's no sign of her.

Ruby: But she can't just have vanished!

Zack: Maybe she's run away.

Mum: Oh dear!

Fred: Shall we phone the police?

Alesha: Hang on – what's that, in between those two trees?

Scott: It looks like a hammock.

Mum: But it's Milly's sheet!

Ruby: It's tied to the trees, just like a hammock!

Zack: What's that under it?

Fred: Lots of apple cores!

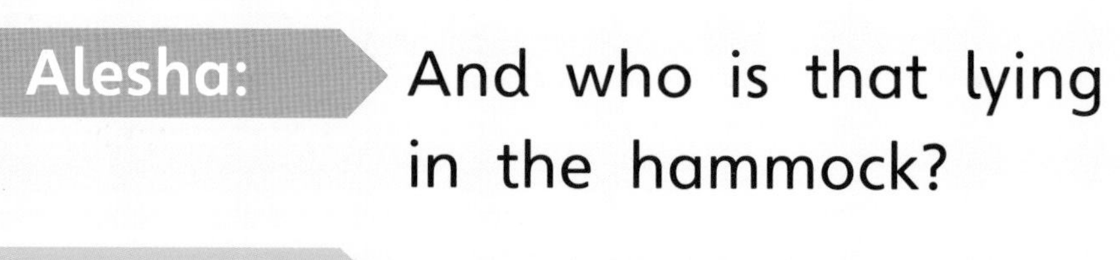

Alesha: And who is that lying in the hammock?

Scott: She's got cushions.

Ruby: And sunglasses.

Zack: And a hat.

Fred: And she's fast asleep!

Mum: It's Milly!

Everyone: WAKE UP, MILLY!